Date Due

Branches Green

BRANCHES GREEN

BY
Lyman
RACHEL FIELD

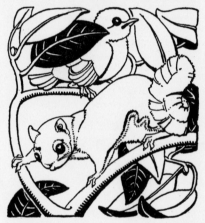

WITH DECORATIONS BY
DOROTHY P. LATHROP

6-8grade

NEW YORK
THE MACMILLAN COMPANY
1934

PRINTED IN THE UNITED STATES OF AMERICA
BY THE STRATFORD PRESS, INC., NEW YORK

For
Anne Parrish
these rhymes

* * *

Faintly the dwindled sea
Hums in the fluted shell.
Dim is the sky's far blue
At the bottom of a well.
Only the thorn is left
Of the early scattered rose;
Only the gilded vane
Marks how the swift wind goes,
And the pressed leaf's brittle bones
Snatched from the pack of time
Are no less frail and dry
Than the echoes of my rhyme.
Take them for shadows then,
For remembered sun and rain,—
Only the mind and heart
May clothe them in green again.

* * *

ACKNOWLEDGMENTS

ACKNOWLEDGMENTS

The following poems were first printed in F.P.A.'s Conning Tower in the *New York Herald Tribune:* "Old Gardener Time," "Prettymarsh," "Epitaph for a Scotch Terrier," "Wild Honey," "An Apology for This Book," "I Want a Pasture," "After Rain," "Spring Signs," "This Afternoon," "Northern Song," "Legend," "Years Ago," "Eighth Street West," "Anniversary." "The Thorn Trees" appeared in the *New York Evening Sun;* "Grandmother's Brook" and "Wild Cranberry" in *The Saturday Review of Literature;* "Early Morning" in *The New Yorker.*

A number of poems have been used in children's magazines: "The Old Music Box," "The Lost Bell," "For a Doll's House" in *Child Life;* "For a Dog Chasing Fireflies," "Gentians May Not Stay," "A Vow in Mid-summer," "Family Pew" in the *American Girl;* "A Rhyme for Trees" in *John Martin's Book.*

Two poems appeared first in textbook form with Ginn and Company, "Ticking Clocks" and "Marooned."

The collection "A Circus Garland" was first printed in The Three Owls column edited by Anne Carroll Moore for the *New York Herald Tribune,* and was later used in The Three Owls, Volume III, published by Coward-McCann.

CONTENTS

[ix]

CONTENTS

[x]

An Apology for This Book

Leaves are scarlet; skies are blue;
I must chirp as crickets do.
All because it is the season
When we need more rhyme than reason!

Times and Places

Old Gardener Time

Old Gardener Time is abroad to-night,
Shuffling through leaves that fell all day.
Out in the dark I can hear his broom
Secretly sweeping the gold and gay;
The pointed scarlet; the rusty brown
In piles that smolder, while crickets shrill,
And summer is only a faint, sweet thread
Of dusty smoke at the window sill.
Warm is my pillow and dreams beguile.
I lie secure in a quiet room,—
But Old Gardener Time is abroad to-night
In the frosty dark with his tireless broom.

Prettymarsh

What is this place that it should bear
A name so salty-sweet and fair?
A name to tease my mind with brown
Tide flats about a scattered town
Of clapboard houses, squarely set
Behind their phlox and mignonette;
Their larkspur, lilies and sweet-peas;
Where wine-glass elms and apple trees
Shake out their shadows on the grass;
Where blue-wheeled carts and hayloads pass,
And ships with patched sails slowly ply
A crooked course when tides are high,
Or tilt their darkened hulls where grow
Keen-smelling weeds when tides are low;
Where Time seems but a shadow traced
Upon the church clock's numbered face.
Dear Prettymarsh, I shall not go
To see if you are really so.
What need, when letters on a sign
Can make you so completely mine?

Snow by Night

Snow is falling to-night,
    The tallest buildings seem
Angular giants dim
    As the texture of a dream.
Snow at the window pane,
    And we who watch it blow,
Slanting and fine and white
    Must whisper:—"Even so
It fell on roofs of old,
    On streets of long ago,
On the watchman calling, 'Twelve
    O' the clock, and a fall of snow!' "

Snow in the City

Snow is out of fashion,
    But it still comes down,
To whiten all the buildings
    In our town;
To dull the noise of traffic;
    To dim each glaring light
With star-shaped feathers
    Of frosty white.
And not the tallest building
    Halfway up the sky;
Or all the trains and busses,
    And taxis scudding by;
And not a million people,
    Not one of them at all,
Can do a thing about the snow
    But let it fall!

Ticking Clocks

The cuckoo clock on the nursery wall
Has a voice that is woody and brown and small,
And all day long in happy rhyme
Its ticks are saying, *Plenty of Time,*
  There's always plenty of Time.

On the mantel over the fireplace
The marble clock with the gilded face
And chimes as sweet as a sea-drowned bell
Says over and over, *Time will tell,*
  Yes, Time will always tell.

The old hall clock with the pendulum
Beats every hour like a drum.
Heavy and deep, from far inside,
Hear how it booms out, *Time and Tide,*
  Solemnly, Time and Tide.

Grandmother's Brook

Grandmother tells me about a brook
    She used to pass on her way to school;
A quick, brown brook with a rushing sound,
    And moss green edges, thick and cool.
When she was the age that I am now
    She would cross over it, stone by stone,
I like to think how she must have looked
    Under the greenery, all alone.

Sometimes I ask her:—"Is it there,
    That brook you played by,—the same, to-day?"
And she says she hasn't a doubt it is—
    It's children who change and go away,

The Old Music Box

It's not the tunes that it can play,
But something else. I can never say
Whether it's more like falling rain
Far, far away, in France or Spain;
Or a hurrying brook, or the delicate din
When a humming bird begins to spin
Its rainbow wings; or the drone of bees,
Or something that is none of these.
But always under the tinkling part,
You can hear it beating like a heart,
Or the tick of tiny fairy clocks
Hidden away in the music box.

Something Told the Wild Geese

Something told the wild geese
   It was time to go.
Though the fields lay golden
   Something whispered,—"Snow."
Leaves were green and stirring,
   Berries, luster-glossed,
But beneath warm feathers
   Something cautioned,—"Frost."
All the sagging orchards
   Steamed with amber spice,
But each wild breast stiffened
   At remembered ice.
Something told the wild geese
   It was time to fly,—
Summer sun was on their wings,
   Winter in their cry.

Four Paws and a Tail

For a Dog Chasing Fireflies

Why do we smile at one who goes
With eager paws and pointing nose;
With rolling eye, and frantic rush
On these small lights mysterious?
Are we more sensible or wise
Because we call them fireflies?
Because from our superior height
We watch you charge each phantom light,
Incredulous, and half afraid,
That such can shine and also fade
Out of your reach to reappear
Ever beyond and never near.
By what sure power do we place
Ourselves above such futile chase,
Who seek more fleeting lights than these
That glitter under darkening trees?

Who are you that can fly,
Or hide in a crumpled leaf;
To whom my hand is a vast
Pink plain of space and wonder?
Who breathed on your sleek, gray coat
That it should be thistledown soft,
And thicker than velvet mullein?
How were your whiskers spun,
More fine than silver thread?
Why are your claws so frail,
Like frost, with as eerie a coldness?
How came your tail to be
Flat as dove's breast-feather?
Who taught you to fold it close
In a curl about your haunches?
Why are your eyes so black,
So restless and ever shining
Under your pointed ears?
And how can a small heart beat
So fast in a tiny body?

The Lost Bell

My dog Trot
Has lost her bell.
Where it rings now
Who can tell?
By berry bramble,
And juniper,
Where grass grows thick
As soft green fur;
Where rabbits scuttle,
And chipmunks scold,
Where sunlight wavers
Through branches old;
From thorny thicket,
And mossy ground,
Have you heard a bell
With a silver sound?
In weedy rock-pool
With sea flung shell,—
Wherever she left it
Trot won't tell!

Epitaph for a Scotch Terrier

Pause a moment by this spot
Whether you have dogs or not.
Here four blunt paws now quiet lie
That once went gayly padding by.
Here rests a tail that never grew
Too limp for making glad to-do.
Here mute, a bell from harness hung,
That often through green woods has rung,
And here a heart that put to shame
Others that pass for such in name.

Early Morning

After the forty troubled days
  And nights of huddled dark;
After the perilous, shifting ways
  Of Noah's crowded Ark,
How frantic must the cloven feet
  Of deer and antelope
Have sped through fern and grasses sweet
  On Ararat's steep slope.

How must the leopard, goat, and hare;
  The chipmunk and the mouse
Have hailed that wood without a snare
  In rapturous carouse.
How must each drooping monkey tail
  With ecstasy have curled;
With what sedate delight the snail
  Have paced a rooted world.

How clear, across the barren waste,
  Flood-swept and watery,
Must every bird in liquid haste
  Have called from bush and tree.
Only the dove, bedraggled, weak,
  Too spent to coo or preen,
Must cling with damp and stubborn beak
  To her one leaf of green.

A Circus Garland

Parade

This is the day the circus comes
With blare of brass, with beating drums,
And clashing cymbals, and with roar
Of wild beasts never heard before
Within town limits. Spick and span
Will shine each gilded cage and van;
Cockades at every horse's head
Will nod, and riders dressed in red
Or blue trot by. There will be floats
In shapes like dragons, thrones and boats,
And clowns on stilts; freaks big and small,
Till leisurely and last of all
Camels and elephants will pass
Beneath our elms, along our grass.

The Performing Seal

Who is so proud
As not to feel
A secret awe
Before a seal
That keeps such sleek
And wet repose
While twirling candles
On his nose?

Acrobat

Surely that is not a man
    Balanced on a thread in air,
But a brightly colored fan
    Folding and unfolding there?

Gunga

With wrinkled hide and great frayed ears,
Gunga the elephant, appears.
Colored like city smoke he goes
As gingerly on blunted toes
As if he held the earth in trust
And feared to hurt the very dust.

Equestrienne

See, they are clearing the sawdust course
For the girl in pink on the milk-white horse.
Her spangles twinkle; his pale flanks shine,
Every hair of his tail is fine
And bright as a comet's; his mane blows free,
And she points a toe and bends a knee,
The while his hoofbeats fall like rain
Over and over and over again.
And nothing that moves on land or sea
Will seem so beautiful to me
As the girl in pink on the milk-white horse
Cantering over the sawdust course.

Epilogue

Nothing now to mark the spot
But a littered vacant lot;
Sawdust in a heap, and there
Where the ring was, grass worn bare
In a circle, scuffed and brown,
And a paper hoop the clown
Made his little dog jump through,
And a pygmy pony-shoe.

Branches Green

The Thorn Trees

The thorn trees hold their berries high
In crowded scarlet to the sky.
No beads so red were ever seen
When gypsies camp upon a green,
Or such a shine spread to the air
On any patterned luster-ware.
The thorn trees have no need to hide
From pasture, road, or countryside.
Too bright of skin and sharp of core,
Theirs is no fruit for housewife's store.
Thornberries need be only gay
To give the heart a holiday.

A Rhyme for Trees

The birch tree's trunk is beautiful,
Whiter than shining breast of gull
Laid to the steep blue slopes of air.
Maples are gay as a county fair
In red and yellow for early frost.
A pine has rugged greenness tossed
On windy branches. A balsam fir
Is thick with needles, spicier
Than scents of ancient Araby.
The elm makes dappled tracery
Of shade on lawn and village street.
The spruce's bark is sticky-sweet.
Horse-chestnut flowers like steeples rise.
A poplar is full of leafy sighs.
In fall the oak spreads a russet dome.
The apple is gnarled as a friendly gnome,
Crooked of bough, twisted of root.
But a mountain ash has fiery fruit,
And who in his pocket hides a spray,
Magic will keep by night and day.

After Rain

See how upon bare twigs they lie,
Raindrops, lately of the sky—
Balls of crystal, rounder far
Than any earthen berries are.
Phantom fruits begot of air
Fashioned for no human fare.

Wild Cranberry

Were these the fairy apples Snow-White knew,
    Scarlet sided and white?
And shall these lips of mine taste magic too,
    And spells, at the first sharp bite?
I never stooped to pick them where they grew,
    Incredible and bright,
But the old tale has taken me anew
And I have half believed it might be true.

Gentians May Not Stay

Gentians may not stay
In accustomed places.
A season, maybe two,
And they must steal away,
Folding up their blue
Fringes secretly
As bands of gypsies do,
Peddling charms and laces
At the edge of frost.
But when they have gone
Woodsmoke lingers there,
Dim and ghostly blue
On the autumn air.
Gentians may not stay,
They are gypsies, too,
Fugitive as lost tunes,
Brief as morning dew.

A Vow in Mid-summer

Now let us sing how purple vetch
    Keeps daisies company,
With devil's paint-brush, copper tipped,
    In fields above the sea.

And let us mark how grasses bow
    Before the wind's swift greeting,
And how the shadows on the hills
    Are dark and lean and fleeting.

But let us never quite forget
    When orange lilies glow,
To bless the hands that set them out
    In dooryards, years ago.

Wild Honey

The wild bees cluster and crowd and hum
In the dooryard's blue delphinium.
They tilt in clover and jostling, fetch
Sweet on sweet from the purple vetch,
With never a pause in their anxious haste,
Making honey no lips shall taste.

What of your golden comb, wild bees,
Stored secure in some ancient tree's
Hidden hollow? What of this sweet
None shall discover? That none shall eat?
What of the treasure none shall find
In the secret places of the mind?

Northwest Window

A Northwest Window

This window opens wide to sky and sea;
   To sand and sunsets and a twisted tree;
And any eye that will may take delight
   In windy blue by day, or moon by night;
In blown dune grass, and lighthouse, white and far,
   That shines at evening like a nearer star.
This window opens wide to sea and sky,
   And who need farther look? Not you, not I.

I Want a Pasture

I want a pasture for next door neighbor;
  The sea to be just across the way.
I want to stand at my door for hours
  Talking and passing the time of day
Unhurried, as country people do
Season on season, a whole year through.

I want to give greeting to frost and sun;
  To gossip with thunder and tides and bees;
To mark the doings of wind in boughs;
  Watch apples redden on crookéd trees.
I want to hail each passing thing
That moves, fleet-footed, by fin, or wing.

I want far islands to grow familiar
  As neighbors' faces; clouds be more plain
Than granite bowlder; than web of spider
  Patterned with intricate drops of rain.
I want to be wise as the oldest star,
Young as the waves and grasses are.

This Afternoon

Now hills retreat in amethyst;
Peaked Sargent wears a cap of mist.
The sun has found a far, white spire
And touched the tip to pagan fire.
In port the sea-turned windows twinkle
Like specks of mica. Lax sails wrinkle
As boats put in. Kelp ruddy shines
To mark the tide's last boundary lines.
In tattered ranks that storm the land
Dark on their point the spruces stand.
Gleaming as shells that shine through foam
Sunset is taking the sea-gulls home.

Heard at Night

The tree-toad's a town crier
    With faint and rusty bell
That through long summer evenings
    Rings out a far "All's well."

And from the swampy thicket
    The frogs croak, like a score
Of old men gathered nightly
    About some village store.

But shrill as ancient fiddle
    Beneath a blindman's bow
Crickets and grasshoppers must play
    The only tune they know.

Spring Signs

Now is the time that hills put on
A smoky blue, untinged with green,
When sorrel-red and cinnamon
In brief possession hold the scene;
When robins, orange breasted, shiver,
And wrens and burnished grackles scold;
When every brook is a rushing river,
And crocus companies brave the cold;
When freshly painted cars speed by,
And dogs and children skip and caper;—
Now is the time when such as I
Must set down rhymes on sheets of paper!

Marooned

Narrow River is salty blue,
   The thorn trees shine and blur.
Along the humped backs of the dunes
   Sand grass grows thick as fur.
Gulls wheel and settle like falling snow,
   White flakes in the summer sun.
But darkly tilted, its mast awry,
   Is an old ship's skeleton,—
Marooned as never a ship should be,
Prow turned inland and stern to sea.

Family Pew

I wonder if my Great-Grandmother felt
 Air half so keen and sweet with salt and bay
On such a summer Sunday as she knelt
 In this old pew and heard the Parson pray?

I wonder if she saw white clouds stream by
 Through that same narrow window, if the trees
Were darkly green against so blue a sky,
 Pointing their tips as solemnly as these?

I wonder if she heard such gay birds sing
 Above the sermon and doxology;
If she was glad for each shrill twittering,
 For hum of bees and boom of distant sea?

Beneath some prim and flower-patterned dress
 Did her heart stir, as mine, to quickened beat?
And was she dumb in sudden thankfulness
 That she was young, and the round earth so sweet?

[43]

Back Country

Wherever there were gaps between
Each steep-set farm, the woods were green
And brown, with shafts of sun that made
Emerald fire in bristling shade.
Dooryard roses hummed with bees.
Cows stood staring, up to their knees
In an old mill pond where no wheels churn.
Sheep, in laurel and clumps of fern,
Grayer than bowlders, moved one way.
Every cart with its load of hay
Had creaking wheels of faded blue
Like the flapping overalls askew
On the canted scarecrow, lone and lorn,
Solemnly guarding his field of corn.
The crossroads sign had tumbled down
So I asked a boy and girl with brown
Bare feet the way when they went by
Quick as rabbits, and twice as shy.

Northern Song

Morning comes over the eastern islands;
Twilight waits in the western hills.
High in the north above my roof-top
Night's starry dipper hangs and spills
Dark and inexhaustible waters,
Oblivion's dew for the restless brain;
Balm for the wakeful; peace for the sleeper,
Sweeter than music, softer than rain.

Certain Days

Years Ago

Years ago and years ago
We gathered ground-pine in the snow,
In a wooded place beyond the glen.
I was eight years old and you were ten.
We wore red mittens and mufflers tied
Up to our noses. A blue-jay cried;
Tree-trunk shadows across the snow
Wavered as blue as indigo.
There were tracks of squirrel and deer and hare,
Delicate claw prints everywhere.
We spoke in whispers it was so still,
And we found a beautiful black crow quill.
Then twilight came and a thread of moon
On December's shortest afternoon.
Lights in the town shone, small and clear,
They were playing carols as we drew near
The old brick church. We called "Hello"
When someone laughed to see us go,
Each like a walking Christmas tree.
"I know a secret," you said to me
By your snowy gate where the hemlock grew,
And I whispered back, "I know one, too."

Legend

Once every year the legend goes,
Before the first faint prick of rose
(Prophetic of a sharper thorn)
Stabs through the east on Christmas morn,
While sleepy folk lie snug abed,
In stable, barn, and narrow shed
No bird or beast that must not stir
From feathered dreams, from drowsy fur,
For in that moment each of them
Is linked to far-off Bethlehem
By some rough-coated ancestor
Who whinnied at the stable door
When Wise Men knocked; by some shy beast
Who hailed strange brightness in the east
With anxious bark, and startled bleat,
With muffled coo, and padding feet;
With soft cries immemorial
Echoed from eave-swung nest and stall.
While from the frosty dark immense,
Doomed to a golden permanence,
The weather-cock may shed his curse
Of traitor's warning, to rehearse
More shrill than carols of the blest
His ancient:—"Christus natus est!"'

I will go walking on Eighth Street
   Now that it's Christmas time
To see the little shops all decked
   Gay as a pantomime.
There will be patchwork and Russian smocks;
   Angels of marzapan;
Green glass bottles and picture books
   In their jackets spick and span.
There will be knickknacks of painted wood;
   Candles for every tree
Stacked at the curb in spicy green
   Bristling and needle-y.
There will be children and dogs about;
   Organ men to play,
And people carrying parcels home,
   Hurrying on their way.
I will go walking on Eighth Street
   From Avenue to "L,"
Seeing the sights of Christmas,
   Smelling each Christmas smell.

For a Doll's House

My mind exactly fits this place
    For, being undersize,
This furniture in proper scale
    Its every want supplies;
The garlands on the rug so gay,
    A rosewood chair to please,
The sofa where a tired mind
    May rest in tufted ease;
A dressing table small enough
    To charm Titania's daughter
With looking glass as round and bright
    As a new-minted quarter;
A lamp in ivory and blue,
    And, since a mind must sup,
A china tea-set, buff and gold,
    With sprigs on every cup.

Anniversary

(For Sheelah, November 12, 1910)

My dear, the crowding seasons shift
    Once more to mid-November,
Your birthday and this the only gift
    I may make you now,—to remember
How still the house was; how rapt we two
    Sat with the book between,
Playmates, and one was I, one you,
    A scarlet dress and a green
In the firelight. Your dark head drooped,
    Like a shadow fell your hair,
And Titania, Bottom, and Oberon trooped
    From the pictured pages there.
Your fingers turning the leaves lay frail
    As frost on a window pane;
So wide your eyes they seemed half the tale;
    Your small voice soft as rain.
Close, yet so far away from me
    In that moment you were, that I
Shrank at some unguessed certainty,
    Lonely, not knowing why.

The Ballad of Spindle-Wood

The Ballad of Spindle-Wood

"I am grown lonely and stiff of joint,"
     Said the Woman of Spindle-Wood,
"Young feet I need to work my will,
     Young hands to serve me food.

Now frost has taken the countryside
     And the blue has left the sea,
I will fetch a Bound-Out Girl from town
     For my winter's company."

Dark tales in the port they told of her,
     The Woman of Spindle-Wood,
Of the snares she laid for souls that strayed,
     To win her livelihood.

Yet her silver clinked with a pleasant sound
     Deep in her leathern sack,
And one went forth, but two returned
     On the pine woods' soundless track.

"Oh, M'am, what for does your chimney smoke
     Rise straight though the trees are bent?"
"Enough that you tend the fire, child,
     Bring wood when this is spent."

"Oh, M'am, what shadows strange are these
That from your mirror peer?
What means this net, these cages set,
These rustlings that I hear?"

"Ask me no questions, Bound-Out Girl,
Go fetch the tea and bread.
Sing with the kettle and you shall have gold
For dower when you are wed.

You shall have gowns of flowery print,
A crimson cloak to wear,
A silver spoon to stir your tea,
Ribbons to bind your hair."

Sweetly the Bound Girl sang and bent
To the fire's russet flame,
But she moved in dread, with a heart of lead,
And fears she dared not name.

Short grew the days, the chill nights long,
Loud gnawed the fierce sea tide.
The Woman of Spindle-Wood slept fast,
But her Bound Girl woke and cried.

She shivered and hid her sleek brown head
   'Neath pillow and counterpane,
For faint and fine as sleet she heard
   The poor trapped souls complain.

She thought of the dangling cages hung
   In the dusty eaves above,
Where never was heard sweet throated bird,
   Wood-pigeon or thrush or dove.

"Oh, God in heaven," the Bound Girl prayed,
   "In pity cherish me,
Who am sore beset in an evil place
   By spells and sorcery."

Alone in the dark she prayed and wept
   Till the red sun climbed the sea,
"Leave off your sighing, poor, caged souls,
   For I will set you free.

Leave off your sighing and hear my vow
   Whoever you may be,—
Evil or good, you shall quit this wood,
   So wait you patiently."

[59]

Through Spindle-Wood the north wind blew,
    Spray froze along the shore,
In the clustered town, sweet cakes grew brown,
    Wreaths hung at every door.

"What troubles you, my Bound-Out Girl,
    That you should stare and sigh?"
"Oh, Mistress, to-night will be Christmas Eve,
    And I'll hear no waits go by.

Lights will shine in the steepled church
    Where the neighbors go to pray,
The rafters ring with their caroling,
    And I these miles away."

"Come, foolish child, here's wine and cake,
    Fruity and dark and sweet,
Prayers and chanting make meager fare,
    So freely drink and eat."

The Woman of Spindle-Wood drank long,
    Down drooped her eyes in sleep,
"God grant she wake not," her Bound Girl prayed,
    "Till I my vow may keep."

Two coals in the dwindling fire there
Watched like a pair of eyes.
To the ladder she crept stealthily
That to the eaves did rise.

Icicle-cold her fingers groped;
She mounted, rung by rung.
Nearer the shadowed rafters loomed
Where the wicker cages hung.

A bat swooped by in the dusty gloom,
Squat spiders wove and spun.
Pale in the dimness gleamed the bones
Of a mouse's skeleton.

On the topmost beam her hand she laid.
Her peering eyes grew wide.
For there in the dark, a heart-shaped spark
In each barred cage she spied.

Brighter than firefly hosts in June
Those little lights did prick
The crow-black shadows round about
Where the dust of years lay thick.

"Fly to your freedom now, poor souls,
    Ere Christmas Day comes in."
She whispered and felt for the nearest cage
    To draw the wooden pin.

Each narrow door at her touch swung wide,
    The lights thronged, one by one.
She made no sound, but went her round,
    Nor paused till her work was done.

She paused not then for drink or food,
    For shoes or cloak or hood;
Fleeter than shadow the Bound Girl crept
    Past the Woman of Spindle-Wood.

Hunched and gray on her wrinkled hands,
    Sleep held her in its grip,
She lay like the gaunt and sea-worn hulk
    Of some long forgotten ship.

"Make haste, poor souls, to seek your rest!"
    She drew the bolt aside.
"I am young to die, who cold may lie,
    And still ere the turn of tide."

Sharp as a whip the sea wind tore
    At the tattered ranks of trees,
But round her head the little lights
    Swarmed like a cloud of bees.

Like golden bees round a summer hive
    They hovered with humming sound,
And violet, bluebell and windflower sprang
    Full blown from the frosty ground.

She moved from bristling tree to tree;
    She took each height and hollow.
With evil croak her mistress woke
    And cursing shrill did follow.

"God save us from her wrath this night,
    Let not her wiles ensnare
Till safely to the church I bring
    These lost souls in my care."

She left the wood; she climbed the hill;
    She passed the crossroads sign;
She saw the lighthouse far at sea,
    And scattered farm lamps shine.

[64]

But the Woman of Spindle-Wood pressed hard
    And closer on her track.
Loud thundered she and furiously
    As wolves in a hungry pack.

"Oh, Souls, each pace she nearer draws,
    My feet grow faint and sore,
My breath is spent with yet a mile
    Between us and the door."

Shrill crowed a cock; a startled hound
    Set up a dismal bay.
"Think not to trick me, Bound-Out Girl,
    Or dearly you shall pay!"

Her mistress like a hurricane
    Bore down with wild careen,
And now they gained the cobbled street,
    Scarce showed a length between.

Within the church the neighbors paled,
    Stricken they knelt and dumb,
The steeple rocked as if the trump
    Of Judgment Day were come.

The prayer upon the parson's lips
    Was drowned in sullen roar,
Then silence came and like a flame
    Strange brightness filled the door.

The neighbors trembled,—" 'Tis some ghost
    Who restless walks," they said,
But all they saw was the Bound-Out Girl
    With small lights round her head.